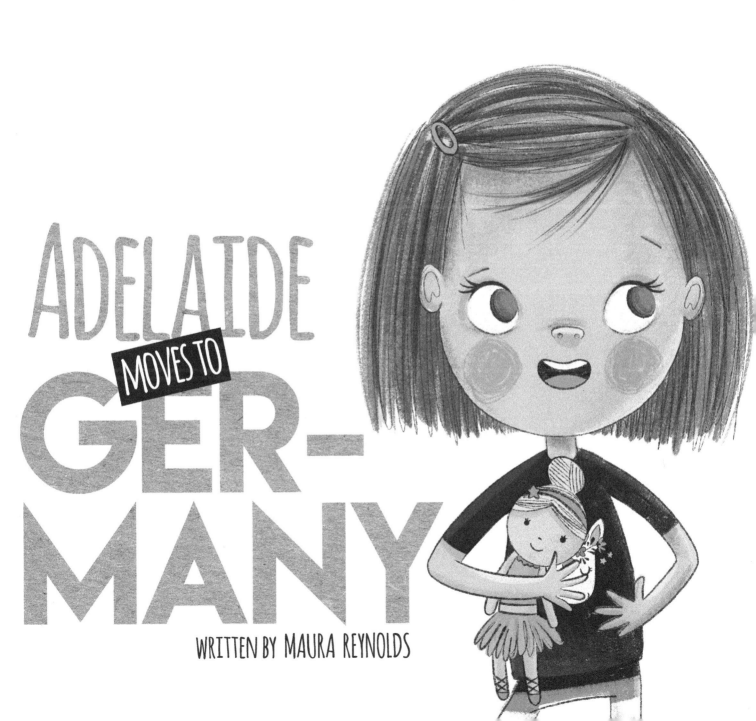

ADELAIDE
MOVES TO
GER-
MANY

WRITTEN BY MAURA REYNOLDS

This book is dedicated to my Dad, Joseph H. Hartough.
His passion to his writing craft of poetry and children's stories
inspired me to be a storyteller on paper. His love and generosity
to me and my children will live for generations to come.

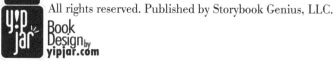
All rights reserved. Published by Storybook Genius, LLC.

Guten Tag!
Hello!

My name is Adelaide.
I used to live in Virginia with my Mom, Dad,
little brother, Leo, and my favorite doll, Kaylin.

Our family is in the United States military.
My Daddy works for the Army.
We move to new places often and meet lots of new people.

The Army is part of our family, just like my cousins, my grandmas, my grandpa and my brother. It is really fun to have such a big family!

We recently moved to Germany,
which is far, far away from Virginia.

I loved all my friends at school in Virginia and
I knew I would make new friends in Germany.

I tried to imagine what they would look like.

Part of my heart was so happy with my friends in Virginia and a little sad to leave them.
Another part of my heart was excited for new friends!

My Dad said that all my new friends in Germany will speak German. And soon I will know lots of new words!

Before we moved, our whole family went to class to learn how to speak in German.

There were so many exciting things that happened
before we moved that I couldn't even count them all!

My Grandma and Grandpa bought a new pink bike for me.
It is one of my very favorite things in the whole world.

I ride it all the time!
I love to ride fast in my purple helmet!

We shipped my bike all the way to Germany!

My Dad said we would get there before it arrived.

Airplanes must fly faster
than bikes can ride!

I got to pick out all the dolls and toys I wanted to keep with me for our trip. I had to pack all my other toys and books into boxes.

My Mom told me to only pick my favorite dolls because I'd have to carry them all by myself onto the plane.

The day we moved away from Virginia,
I woke up and the first thing I saw was my suitcase.

My little brother and I got to stay in our
jammies all day. This was a special day,
the day we said goodbye to our house.

I felt sad saying goodbye to our big,
fun house in Virginia.
The house that I loved.

With a big smile and tears in my eyes,
I gave our big tree one last big hug.
I was happy and sad all at the same time!

My dad gave me a great big hug and told me that it was okay to feel sad and that it is awesome that I have so many great memories of Virginia to hold in my heart.

Our house was all packed up and our moving van was already on its way to meet the ship that would take all of our things to Germany.

My Dad said it would take longer for our things to get there, so the moving van left before us. We shipped everything except what fit in our suitcases and backpacks. And of course, our dog Kristoff, who was coming on the plane with us!

The day I said goodbye to my friends, my home and Virginia was sad plus exciting.
I could not wait to meet my new friends, our new home and Germany!
But my heart felt funny letting go of the people and places I knew and loved
so I began to use my imagination to think about all the new people and places
I had yet to meet.

I felt so glad to have had my backpack and my family with me as we drove off to the airport on our way to Germany!

There is so much that I have seen since landing in Germany.
Do you see that castle in the hills?
I cannot wait to tell you everything...

...but it will have to wait for now.
We are off to our new home!

Tschüss!
Bye!

THIS WAY
THAT WAY

ADVENTURE
BUDDIES

CHOO-
CHOO
CHOO

Germany is FUN

there's a baby in the family

Photo credit Jenelle Botts Photography

It's your turn!
Where have you traveled?
Where do you want to travel?
Draw, write, paste or color your
memories or ideas, here!

CPSIA information can be obtained
at www.ICGtesting.com
Printed in the USA
LVHW072158170821
695428LV00021B/119

9 781952 954757